Dan

Written by Rozanne Lanczak Williams
Created by Sue Lewis
Illustrated by Patty Briles

Creative Teaching Press

Dan and Dot
© 2002 Creative Teaching Press, Inc.
Written by Rozanne Lanczak Williams
Illustrated by Patty Briles
Project Manager: Sue Lewis
Project Director: Carolea Williams

Published in the United States of America by:
Creative Teaching Press, Inc.
P.O. Box 2723
Huntington Beach, CA 92647-0723

All rights reserved. No part of this book may be reproduced in any form without
the written permission of Creative Teaching Press, Inc.

ISBN: 1-57471-873-8
CTP 3239

Dan and Dot spot a bag.

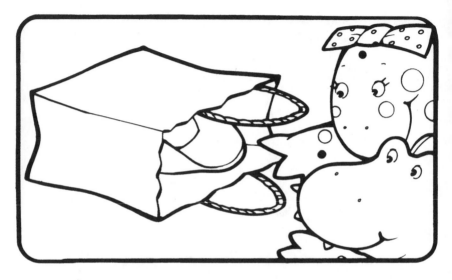

Dan and Dot spot a hat
in the bag.

Dan and Dot spot a cat
in the hat in the bag.

Dan and Dot spot pants on the cat in the hat in the bag.

The cat in the hat
spots a rat!

The cat hops out of the bag.

The cat jogs after the rat.
Dan and Dot jog after the cat.

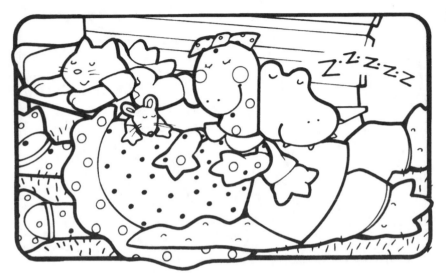

Dan, Dot, the cat, and the rat stop for a nap.

Create your own book!

Write about other things that Dan and Dot spot when they go on a walk. Use words with short *a* or *o*, or other words that you know.

Words in *Dan and Dot*

Short *a* and *o*

Dan	spots
and	stop
bag	jog
cat	jogs
hat	hops
rat	
nap	
after	
pants	
Dot	
spot	

High-Frequency Words

a
in
the
on
out
of
for